MARITAL BLISS

AND OTHER OXYMORONS

by Joe Kohl

CCC PUBLICATIONS

Published by

CCC Publications
1111 Rancho Conejo Blvd.
Suites 411 & 412
Newbury Park, CA 91320

Manufactured in the United States of America

Cover & interior art by Joe Kohl

Cover & Interior Illustrations © 1994 CCC Publications

Interior layout by Oasis Graphics

ISBN: 0-918259-75-4

If your local U.S. bookstore is out of stock, copies of this book may be obtained by mailing check or money order for $4.99 per book (plus $2.50 to cover postage and handling) to: CCC Publications; 1111 Rancho Conejo Blvd.; Suites 411 & 412; Newbury Park, CA 91320

Pre-Publication Edition 5/94

First Printing 4/95

"I suppose you're gonna talk about bowling all evening!"

"I sent out the laundry."

"Did you remember the mousse?"

"He'll take something in a very fat !"

"Of course we share the chores...
I cook and he eats."

"Here it is...Page 67...'<u>Common Mistakes</u>.'"

"I'm sorry but I have to let you go as my secretary...
however, I'm still keeping you on as my husband."

"The secret to success? Gosh you'll have to ask
my wife about that."

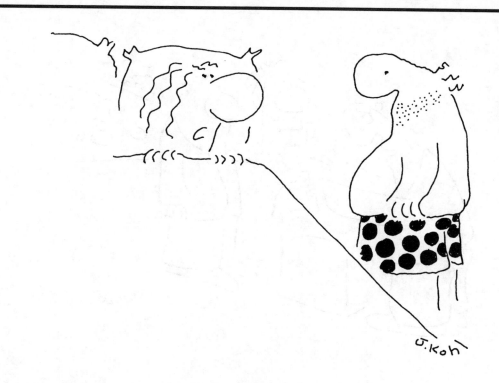

"I'm not in the mood anymore."

"Before I pronounce you husband and wife, if you'll just sign this disclaimer..."

"Why can't I get a raise in my allowance?
You gave daddy a raise in <u>his</u> allowance."

"I think it's pretty serious, Doctor...He slept through the game."

"Just think, Arnold...Five years ago <u>today</u>...and it seems like only yesterday we got the divorce."

"...and here's the part when Fred realized he forgot to take the lens cap off the camcorder."

"Al <u>has</u> had other women...Unfortunately they keep sending him back."

"Oh yeah?!! Well **I** apologized **<u>FIRST</u>**!"

"What's for supper, Dear!"

"Don and I rarely fight.
Then again, we rarely talk."

"Okay, Harriet!! Who is he?"

"...and do you take this man to be
your first husband?"

"The Smedleys' divorce just came through and we've been invited
to the reception next Saturday!"

"This happens everytime someone asks to speak to the head of the household."

"Frank...I want a divorce!"

"I left a message on your machine."

"Sometimes I wish these magazines wouldn't run 'compatibility' tests."

"You've been faking it, haven't you?"

"And do you Carol promise to come straight home from work everyday, cook, clean, do dishes, shop, dust, do laundry, mop floors, vacuum,..."

"You'll have to excuse the mess...
I have a working husband."

"But you just <u>can't</u> leave me, dear...Not after I changed for you and all!!"

"Harriette! Where's my tossed salad?!!"

"'Better or worse' and 'richer or poorer' are not 'choices.'"

"But I don't need a good reason to leave you...After all, I didn't have a good reason to marry you."

"Sorry...I can only repair the TV."

"If anyone feels the bride could do better, speak now or..."

"What's happened to us, Charles? It seems
the fun has gone out of our marriage."

"$47.50 to find out it wasn't plugged in!!!"

"I suppose this is going to be another one of those 'hop on, hop off' nights."

"Yes I know...You've got another pair just like it."

"Would you mind taking out the rubbish between seasons?"

"He's the spitting image of his daddy."

"No, this <u>doesn't</u> mean I'm leaving...They're your bags...
it means <u>you're</u> leaving."

"By the way...I fixed your hair dryer yesterday."

"Leftovers already?"

"Very funny, Phyllis!"

"Of <u>course</u> I have a sense of humor...
I married <u>you</u>!"

"Good news!! I beat my last time by
a minute and seventeen seconds!!!"

"I just don't understand it...One day, during halftime, she just
stuck a note to my six-pack and left."

"All those in favor of Daddy getting a vasectomy
raise your hand."

J. Kohl

"You've had your little joke...Now hang that picture of my mother up <u>right</u>!!!"

"Then again, if it **DID** rain, my hair would
get all frizzy."

"Dammit Martha! You've been holding the
map upside down!!"

"Some <u>romantic</u> you are!"

"Sometimes, Fred, I don't think you listen to
a word I say!"

"I hope you realize this is gonna raise our car insurance premium!!"

TITLES BY CCC PUBLICATIONS

Retail $4.99

POSITIVELY PREGNANT
SIGNS YOUR SEX LIFE IS DEAD
WHY MEN DON'T HAVE A CLUE
40 AND HOLDING YOUR OWN
CAN SEX IMPROVE YOUR GOLF?
THE COMPLETE BOOGER BOOK
THINGS YOU CAN DO WITH A USELESS MAN
FLYING FUNNIES
MARITAL BLISS & OXYMORONS
THE VERY VERY SEXY ADULT DOT-TO-DOT BOOK
THE DEFINITIVE FART BOOK
THE COMPLETE WIMP'S GUIDE TO SEX
THE CAT OWNER'S SHAPE UP MANUAL
PMS CRAZED: TOUCH ME AND I'LL KILL YOU!
RETIRED: LET THE GAMES BEGIN
MALE BASHING: WOMEN'S FAVORITE PASTIME
THE OFFICE FROM HELL
FOOD & SEX
FITNESS FANATICS
YOUNGER MEN ARE BETTER THAN RETIN-A
BUT OSSIFER, IT'S NOT MY FAULT

Retail $4.95

1001 WAYS TO PROCRASTINATE
THE WORLD'S GREATEST PUT-DOWN LINES
HORMONES FROM HELL II
SHARING THE ROAD WITH IDIOTS
THE GREATEST ANSWERING MACHINE MESSAGES
    OF ALL TIME
WHAT DO WE DO NOW?? (A Guide For New Parents)
HOW TO TALK YOU WAY OUT OF A TRAFFIC TICKET
THE BOTTOM HALF (How To Spot Incompetent
    Professionals)
LIFE'S MOST EMBARRASSING MOMENTS
HOW TO ENTERTAIN PEOPLE YOU HATE
YOUR GUIDE TO CORPORATE SURVIVAL
THE SUPERIOR PERSON'S GUIDE TO EVERYDAY
    IRRITATIONS
GIFTING RIGHT

Retail $5.95

50 WAYS TO HUSTLE YOUR FRIENDS ($5.99)
HORMONES FROM HELL
HUSBANDS FROM HELL
KILLER BRAS & Other Hazards Of The 50's
IT'S BETTER TO BE OVER THE HILL THAN UNDER IT
HOW TO REALLY PARTY!!!
WORK SUCKS!
THE PEOPLE WATCHER'S FIRLD GUIDE
THE UNOFFICIAL WOMEN'S DIVORCE GUIDE
THE ABSOLUTE LAST CHANCE DIET BOOK
FOR MEN ONLY (How To Survive Marriage)
THE UGLY TRUTH ABOUT MEN
NEVER A DULL CARD
RED HOT MONOGAMY
   (In Just 60 Seconds A Day) ($6.95)

Retail $3.95

YOU KNOW YOU'RE AN OLD FART WHEN...
NO HANG-UPS
NO HANG-UPS II
NO HANG-UPS III
GETTING EVEN WITH THE ANSWERING MACHINE
HOW TO SUCCEED IN SINGLES BARS
HOW TO GET EVEN WITH YOUR EXES
TOTALLY OUTRAGEOUS BUMPER-SNICKERS ($2.95)

NO HANG-UPS – CASSETTES Retail $4.98

Vol. I: GENERAL MESSAGES (Female)
Vol. I: GENERAL MESSAGES (Male)
Vol. II: BUSINESS MESSAGES (Female)
Vol. II: BUSINESS MESSAGES (Male)
Vol. III: 'R' RATED MESSAGES (Female)
Vol. III: 'R' RATED MESSAGES (Male)
Vol. IV: SOUND EFFECTS ONLY
Vol. V: CELEBRI-TEASE